For Grade
6

Write on Target

Using Graphic Organizers to Improve Writing Skills

Written By:
Yolande F. Grizinski, Ed.D.
Leslie Holzhauser-Peters, MS, CCC-SP

Show What You Know®
Publishing

Published By:
Show What You Know® Publishing
A Division of Englefield & Associates, Inc.
P.O. Box 341348
Columbus, OH 43234-1348
1-877-PASSING (727-7464)

www.showwhatyouknowpublishing.com

Printed in the United States of America
12 11 10   20 19 18 17 16 15 14 13 12 11 10 9 8 7 6 5 4 3

ISBN: 1-59230-157-6

About the Authors

Yolande F. Grizinski received a Bachelor's degree from Miami University, a Master's degree from Wright State University, and a Doctor of Education from the University of Cincinnati. She has worked in public education for thirty years as a curriculum consultant in the areas of language arts with a focus on writing assessment. She is currently the Assistant Superintendent of the Warren County Educational Service Center in Lebanon, Ohio.

Leslie Holzhauser-Peters holds a Bachelor's degree from the University of Cincinnati and Master's degree from Miami University. She has twenty-seven years of experience working in public schools in Special Education and as a Speech-language pathologist, as a Supervisor, and currently as a Curriculum Consultant. Her areas of expertise are language, literacy, and intervention.

The authors met at the Warren County Educational Service Center in Lebanon, Ohio. There they developed and implemented a host of language arts initiatives including a large-scale writing assessment. They have given numerous presentations on the five communication processes and standards-based assessment.

Acknowledgements

Show What You Know® Publishing acknowledges the following for their efforts in making this assessment material available for students, parents, and teachers.

Cindi Englefield, President/Publisher
Eloise Boehm-Sasala, Vice President/Managing Editor
Lainie Burke Rosenthal, Project Editor/Graphic Designer
Erin McDonald, Project Editor
Christine Filippetti, Project Editor
Jill Borish, Project Editor
Charles V. Jackson, Project Editor
Heather Holliday, Project Editor
Jennifer Harney, Illustrator/Cover Designer

© 2005 Englefield & Associates, Inc.

Table of Contents

The Narrative Communication Process

(Fictional Narrative and Personal Experience Narrative)

What is the Narrative Communication Process?

The purpose of the narrative communication process is to tell a story. There are two kinds of narrative communication: a fictional narrative and a personal experience narrative.

A **fictional narrative** is a made-up story from your imagination. Fictional narratives are not true.

In a **personal experience narrative**, you write about something that has happened to you, or something that could have happened to you in real life.

Features of a Fictional Narrative

* A fictional narrative is a made-up story.

* A fictional narrative usually contains a problem that characters in the story need to solve.

Features of the Personal Experience Narrative

* A personal experience narrative is an "all about me" story.

* A personal experience narrative is usually told in the first person ("I").

* A personal experience narrative focuses on an event that could have happened, or has happened, to you in real life.

Writing Activity 1: Fictional Narrative
(A Made-Up Story)

Step
1

Follow along as the fictional narrative "Lucky" is read aloud.

Lucky

Lucky was not just any dog; Lucky was Jeremy's best friend. "Before you know it, that dog will be sitting down to dinner with the entire family," said Jeremy's mother as she tried to hide her smile. "How many times do I have to tell you? Lucky is just a dog." Since the stray golden retriever found his way to Jeremy's front porch four years ago, Lucky and the boy were inseparable.

Early one Monday morning, Jeremy sleepily sifted out the few bits of cereal left floating in his bowl full of milk. Lucky gently placed one paw in his owner's lap. "All right, boy, you can finish the rest." The golden retriever lapped up the sweet milk and looked at Jeremy with his large, brown eyes that always seemed to say, "Thank you, friend."

Before rushing off to school, Jeremy hugged Lucky good-bye on his way out the door. He locked the gate behind him as he ran toward the rumbling, yellow school bus that stood waiting for him.

Upon returning home that afternoon, Jeremy realized something was terribly wrong. The gate was open, and Lucky was gone! Jeremy dropped his books and began to run down the street shouting for Lucky. He called Lucky's name until his throat was sore. He stopped at every house in the neighborhood, but no one had seen Lucky. Jeremy somberly returned home.

At dinner, Jeremy pushed the mashed potatoes around on his blue plate; he could hardly look out the window at the empty yard. "Go on, see if you can find Lucky before dark," Jeremy's mother said reluctantly as she took his plate from the table.

Remembering the times he and Lucky played ball and swam in the lake, Jeremy quickly peddled toward the water. Lucky had always enjoyed playing there. When Jeremy reached the lake, he called out Lucky's name, desperate to find his friend. From behind a cluster of cattails came the sound of a deep bark. When the dog appeared, he was covered with mud that he eagerly shared with a smiling Jeremy. "Let's go home, boy." Lucky ran alongside Jeremy's bike as they traveled home. Jeremy realized how "lucky" he was to find his Lucky.

Step
2

There are several things to keep in mind as you plan and write your own fictional narrative. Remember, a good fictional narrative has the following parts:

- a title that fits the story

- a character or characters you can picture in your mind

- a problem that a character needs to solve

- a beginning, a middle, and an end (think about what happens first, next, then, and finally)

Step
3

Use the following prompt to complete the prewriting and writing activities:

> **Write a fictional narrative. Your narrative begins when your main character is walking in the woods and hears a noise coming from the treetops. Tell what happens in the story.**

Step
4

Complete the graphic organizer on the next page as your prewriting activity. Use your graphic organizer to help you think through your fictional narrative.

Fictional Narrative

A Made-Up Story

Title: _____

Who:
Where:
When:

What Is the Problem?

What Happened?	**First:**

What Happened?	**Next:**

What Happened?	**Then:**

Finally:

Use the information from your graphic organizer to complete your fictional narrative.

Writing Activity 1

Step

5

_____

_____

_____

_____

_____

_____

_____

_____

_____

_____

_____

_____

_____

_____

_____

_____

_____

_____

_____

_____

_____

If you need more room, continue on the next page.

Writing Activity 1

Step

5

_____

_____

_____

_____

_____

_____

_____

_____

_____

_____

_____

_____

_____

_____

_____

_____

_____

_____

_____

_____

_____

_____

Step

6

The checklist shows what your best fictional narrative must include. Use the checklist below to review your work.

Checklist for Writing Activity 1

☐ My story has a title.

☐ My characters have names.

☐ My story begins when the main character hears a noise in the woods.

☐ My story gives details about what happened after my main character hears the noise.

☐ My fictional narrative is well organized and complete.

☐ I try to spell words correctly.

☐ I use words that make my meaning clear. I do not use the same words over and over.

☐ I use correct punctuation and capitalization.

☐ I have written my story so the reader can read my print or cursive writing.

Writing Activity 2: Fictional Narrative
(A Made-Up Story)

Step
1
Follow along as the fictional narrative "Lions and Tigers and Cheetahs" is read aloud.

Lions and Tigers and Cheetahs

Sitting at her desk, Amanda opened her science book to a picture of her favorite animal, the cheetah. Deep in thought, she traced her finger around the edge of the spotted cat's photograph. Amanda was startled as her teacher called the class to line up for the field trip to the zoo. With sack lunches, cool drinks, and comfortable shoes, the class started on their journey. Walking among her classmates, Amanda heard her spending money for the zoo gift shop jingling in her pocket.

The zoo was divided into continents: Australia, Asia, North America, Africa, and South America. Amanda was anxious to see everything, but she really wanted to see the fascinating cheetah. Amanda followed along several pathways as she passed African elephants, wildebeests, giraffes, and the rare black rhinoceros.

The pathway eventually led Amanda to a sign with the small black letters that read "CHEETAH." As she approached the exhibit area, she saw a spotted animal sitting in the tall grass. She watched as the cheetah stood and stretched its long, thin legs. It looked just like its photograph with small, rounded ears and a narrow, white chest. Its coat was yellowish-gray with solid, black spots. Amanda noticed a dark streak on the animal's face extending from the corner of each eye to its upper lip.

Suddenly, the cheetah began to run fast, then faster. Its legs seemed to dig into the earth as it became a blur before her eyes. The magnificent cheetah ran across the land with incredible speed. The animal suddenly stopped at the crest of the hill and turned toward Amanda. She and the animal locked eyes for a brief moment before the cheetah disappeared over the small mound of earth. She gasped and silently waved goodbye.

The class ended their field trip with a visit to the gift shop. It was filled with rubber snakes, koala stuffed animals, board games, and books on every possible animal topic. Amanda looked around and noticed a jar wrapped with a cheetah's picture. A small sign pleaded, "Help the endangered cheetah." Amanda fingered the money from her pocket. She carefully put the entire amount into the jar and whispered, "What a beautiful animal. It's so sad the cheetahs are almost extinct."

Step
2

There are several things to keep in mind as you plan and write your own fictional narrative. Remember, a good fictional narrative has the following parts:

- a title that fits the story

- a character or characters you can picture in your mind

- a problem that a character needs to solve

- a beginning, a middle, and an end (think about what happens first, next, then, and finally)

Step
3

Use the following prompt to complete the prewriting and writing activities:

> **Write a fictional narrative. Your characters will have the opportunity to meet a famous musical entertainer, television personality, book character, author, or historical figure. Tell a story about what happens to your characters when they meet this famous person.**

Step
4

Complete the graphic organizer on the next page as your prewriting activity. Use your graphic organizer to help you think through your fictional narrative.

Fictional Narrative

A Made-Up Story

Title: _____

Who:
Where:
When:

What Is the Problem?

What Happened?	**First:**

What Happened?	**Next:**

What Happened?	**Then:**

Finally:

Use the information from your graphic organizer to complete your fictional narrative.

Writing Activity 2

Step

5

_____

_____

_____

_____

_____

_____

_____

_____

_____

_____

_____

_____

_____

_____

_____

_____

_____

_____

_____

_____

_____

_____

If you need more room, continue on the next page.

Writing Activity 2

Step

5

     COPYING IS PROHIBITED   © 2005 Englefield & Associates, Inc.

Step

6

The checklist shows what your best fictional narrative must include. Use the checklist below to review your work.

Checklist for Writing Activity 2

☐ My story has a title.

☐ My characters have names.

☐ My story gives the name of the famous person the characters meet.

☐ My story tells what happens when my characters meet the famous person.

☐ My fictional narrative is well organized and complete.

☐ I try to spell words correctly.

☐ I use words that make my meaning clear. I do not use the same words over and over.

☐ I use correct punctuation and capitalization.

☐ I have written my story so that my reader can read my print or cursive writing.

Writing Activity 3: Personal Experience Narrative
(A Story About Me)

Step 1   Follow along as the personal experience narrative "The Big Change" is read aloud.

The Big Change

We pulled up to the gigantic brick building, and I slowly opened the van door, pushing myself out onto the sidewalk. "Bye," I said dejectedly.

"Have a great day," my mom replied cheerfully when I slammed the heavy passenger side door shut. I watched our van slowly creep out of the parking lot. I turned around to see a long row of steps leading up to two enormous wooden doors. Unfamiliar students rushed by me, laughing and talking, making their way into the building. I urged my legs forward and up the numerous steps. I shakily reached to pull the handle of the left door, but it flung open without my touching it. A stream of new faces brushed past me and down the stairs. "New girl," I heard someone say as I quickly made my way through the door on the right.

I stepped through to see people weaving through the long hallway. Lockers surrounded me as I hurried through the noise and sea of faces. My eye caught a short blonde girl smiling at me from down the corridor. Making my way toward her, I noticed she was standing under a sign that said "Guidance Office" in bold, white letters.

"I'm Ashley," she said, warmly giving me a smile. "Are you Karen? I have heard so much about you," she declared, not giving me a chance to answer. "I volunteered to show you around. I was new at this school last year and felt really nervous about my first day. I am here to make your first day a little easier."

"Thanks," I stammered. "I have no idea where to go." My heart rate slowed. I felt better and less nervous than when I first arrived. Ashley showed me around the entire day. She introduced me to all my new teachers and classmates. The other students were very friendly, and I felt at ease in my new school. Ashley was quick to let me know about an important school tradition, "Always use the right door. Whether you're entering or exiting, you'll always be in the 'right' if you use the right door." We both laughed when I told her I learned that lesson the hard way. Maybe this new school won't be so bad after all, I thought to myself.

Step
2

There are several things to keep in mind as you plan and write your own personal experience narrative. Write about something that could or did happen to you in your life. The prewriting graphic organizer will help you get ideas for your story. Remember, a good personal experience narrative has the following parts:

- a title that fits the story

- people you know, or events, special times, and memories that did or could have happened to you in real life

- a beginning, a middle, and an end (think about what happens first, next, then, and finally)

Step
3

Use the following prompt to complete the prewriting and writing activities:

> **You arrived home from school and opened the door. You were not prepared for the big surprise that happened to you next. Tell a story to a friend about this surprising time.**

Step
4

Complete the graphic organizer on the next page as your prewriting activity. Use your graphic organizer to help you think through your personal experience narrative.

Personal Experience Narrative

A Story About Me

Title: _____

Who was there?	
Where did it happen?	
When did it happen?	

What Happened? | **First:**

What Happened? | **Next:**

What Happened? | **Then:**

Finally:

Use the information from your graphic organizer to complete your personal experience narrative.

Writing Activity 3

Step

5

_____

_____

_____

_____

_____

_____

_____

_____

_____

_____

_____

_____

_____

_____

_____

_____

_____

_____

_____

_____

_____

If you need more room, continue on the next page.

Writing Activity 3

Step

5

_____

_____

_____

_____

_____

_____

_____

_____

_____

_____

_____

_____

_____

_____

_____

_____

_____

_____

_____

_____

_____

_____

_____

               © 2005 Englefield & Associates, Inc.

Step
6

The checklist shows what your best personal experience narrative must include. Use the checklist below to review your work.

Checklist for Writing Activity 3

☐ My story has a title.

☐ My story is about a time when I was surprised.

☐ My story begins when I open the door.

☐ My story gives details about why I was surprised.

☐ My story has a beginning, middle, and end.

☐ My personal experience narrative is well organized and complete.

☐ I try to spell words correctly.

☐ I use words that make my meaning clear. I do not use the same words over and over.

☐ I use correct punctuation and capitalization.

☐ I have written my story so that my reader can read my print or cursive writing.

Writing Activity 4: Personal Experience Narrative
(A Story About Me)

Step

1

Follow along as the personal experience narrative "Yosemite" is read aloud.

Yosemite

As Terrance's dad drove us closer to Yosemite National Park, I was so excited. I had never been out West before. As the car slid past the park's entrance, I pressed my face against the window to take in the scenery. This was not like the parks back in Cleveland. Even the metro parks, which I always thought were pretty big, were small compared to Yosemite. "Over 700,000 acres in size," Terrance's mom read from a sign.

Terrance's dad drove deep into the park, then stopped at a place called Crane's Flat. Terrance and I leapt from our seats; we were so glad to stand and stretch after that long car ride. It felt like we had been in the car for a month straight! I was elated when Terrance's parents told us we were walking to Tuolumne Grove. I had no idea what Tuolumne Grove was, but I was happy we didn't have to be in the car to get there.

With our feet in comfortable shoes and packs on our backs, we headed for the grove. Terrance and I kept our eyes on the ground. We were looking for insects. Terrance hoped to find some intriguing creatures he had never seen before for his collection. We were so busy bug hunting, we did not notice we were falling behind his parents.

Walking deeper into the grove, the sun seemed to be disappearing, so I looked up. I nudged Terrance, who was busy looking at a beetle. Our mouths dropped. We were surrounded by a forest of the biggest trees I had ever seen, and the Smiths were nowhere to be found. I started to panic. Yosemite was so big. If we're lost, no one will ever find us, I thought. I should have stayed closer to Terrance's parents. What would my parents say if the Smith's came home without me?

"Hey guys, over here," I heard Mrs. Smith call. We both looked around but didn't see her anywhere. She called again, but I still couldn't spot her. When I heard Mr. Smith laughing, I turned in his direction. Terrance's parents were walking around a giant sequoia. The tree had to be 75 feet around! I felt pretty stupid for being so worried, but I was relieved to see them. Terrance's mom took my picture next to the giant trees. I couldn't wait to show the picture to my family, but I knew they'd laugh when I told them about losing Terrance's parents behind a tree.

Tall Tree Forest

Step
2

There are several things to keep in mind as you plan and write your own personal experience narrative. Write about something that could or did happen to you in your life. The prewriting graphic organizer will help you get ideas for your story. Remember, a good personal experience narrative has the following parts:

- a title that fits the story

- people you know, or events, special times, and memories that did or could have happened to you in real life

- a beginning, a middle, and an end (think about what happens first, next, then, and finally)

Step
3

Use the following prompt to complete the prewriting and writing activities:

> **Think about something that happened when you were younger. Choose a story that you remember or one you have heard from family or friends. Tell the story to a friend so that he or she can experience that memorable time.**

Step
4

Complete the graphic organizer on the next page as your prewriting activity. Use your graphic organizer to help you think through your personal experience narrative.

Personal Experience Narrative

A Story About Me

Title: _____

Who was there?
Where did it happen?
When did it happen?

What Happened? | **First:** |

What Happened? | **Next:** |

What Happened? | **Then:** |

| **Finally:** |

Use the information from your graphic organizer to complete your personal experience narrative.

Writing Activity 4

Step

5

If you need more room, continue on the next page.

Writing Activity 4

Step

5

_____

_____

_____

_____

_____

_____

_____

_____

_____

_____

_____

_____

_____

_____

_____

_____

_____

_____

_____

_____

_____

_____

_____

Step 6 The checklist shows what your best personal experience narrative must include. Use the checklist below to review your work.

Checklist for Writing Activity 4

- ☐ My story has a title.

- ☐ My story is about an experience that happened to me when I was younger.

- ☐ My story includes details about what happened.

- ☐ My story has a beginning, middle, and end.

- ☐ My personal experience narrative is well organized and complete.

- ☐ I try to spell words correctly.

- ☐ I use words that make my meaning clear. I do not use the same words over and over.

- ☐ I use correct punctuation and capitalization.

- ☐ I have written my story so that my reader can read my print or cursive writing.

2 The Descriptive Communication Process

(Journal and Descriptive Letter)

What is the Descriptive Communication Process?

The purpose of the descriptive communication process is to create a picture with details that describe a person, place, or thing. You should write descriptions when you want to let readers know how something looks, feels, sounds, tastes, or smells. Two examples of descriptive communication are a journal and a letter.

A **journal** is like a diary. You record your thoughts, ideas, and notes in journals. Some things you may write about in journals include: memories, hobbies, current events, questions, pets, plans, hopes, discoveries, and personal news.

A **descriptive letter** includes a greeting, a body, and a closing. When you write a letter, you are writing to a particular person or group.

Features of a Journal

- The writer of the journal is the audience. You are writing for yourself.
- The purpose of a journal is to record thoughts, feelings, and personal events.
- Journals are usually written in paragraph form.

Features of a Descriptive Letter

- The audience of a letter is a particular person or group to which you are writing.
- Letters are used to communicate.
- Letters contain a greeting, body, and closing.
- Letters are written with a particular purpose.

Writing Activity 5: A Descriptive Journal

Step

1

Follow along as this November 12, 2005, journal entry is read aloud.

November 12, 2005
Journal Entry

Today was one of those days to remember. It was a day filled with life's simple pleasures. Awakening, I peeked out from under my soft comforter to realize I had time to spare before my alarm would go off. The house was so quiet, nothing like most mornings when I wake up late and rush around, getting dressed without a moment to spare.

As I leisurely proceeded to dress, the sounds of life in the room next to mine pierced the silence. A warm, mouthwatering aroma led me down to the kitchen, and there it was, a breakfast like no other: three pieces of golden French toast oozing with syrup next to crisp strips of bacon. A tall glass of apple juice sat glistening next to the plate. Mom stood over the stove flipping more French toast. She was so excited to have a day off; she celebrated by preparing a morning feast.

Turning the combination on my middle school locker, I remembered it was a special schedule day; there was no citizenship and no science. What a relief! And I could not believe my eyes when the cafeteria served pizza, my favorite, for lunch.

The special schedule meant fewer classes and no homework! When I got home there was time to relax, talk on the phone, and chat online. Mom even let me stay up an hour later than usual.

After watching some TV, I headed for my cave. I put on my favorite pajamas and sunk into my mattress. I pulled my crisp, cool sheets and thick comforter around me and thought about the day.

I want to remember how great a day can be if I just enjoy the simple things. If I just appreciate the simple things, maybe every day can be a special one.

Step
2

There are several things to keep in mind as you plan and write your journal entry. Remember, a good journal entry has the following parts:

- a date

- a description of the sights and sounds of the events or people

- a description of your feelings

- a beginning, a middle, and an end

Step
3

Use the following prompt to complete the prewriting and writing activities:

> **You are thinking about someone who has made a difference in your life. In your journal, describe a special time you spent with this person so you will always remember this important time.**

Step
4

Complete the graphic organizer on the next page as your prewriting activity. Use your graphic organizer to help you think through your journal entry.

Journal Entry

What day will you write about in your journal entry?

Why are you writing about this day?

Who was there?

Where did it happen?

When did it happen?

What Happened?	First:

What Happened?	Next:

What Happened?	Then:

Finally:

How did it make you and others feel?

    © 2005 Englefield & Associates, Inc.

Use the information from your graphic organizer to complete your journal entry.

Writing Activity 5

Step

5

If you need more room, continue on the next page.

Writing Activity 5

Step

5

_____

_____

_____

_____

_____

_____

_____

_____

_____

_____

_____

_____

_____

_____

_____

_____

_____

_____

_____

_____

_____

_____

_____

Step

6

The checklist shows what your best journal entry must include. Use the checklist below to review your work.

Checklist for Writing Activity 5

☐ My journal entry has a date.

☐ I describe a person who has made a difference in my life.

☐ I include details about how this person looks, sounds, and so on.

☐ I tell how this person made a difference in my life.

☐ My journal entry has a beginning, middle, and end.

☐ My journal entry is well organized and complete.

☐ I try to spell words correctly.

☐ I use words that make my meaning clear. I do not use the same words over and over.

☐ I use correct punctuation and capitalization.

☐ I have written my journal entry so the reader can read my print or cursive writing.

Writing Activity 6: A Descriptive Journal

Step
1   Follow along as the July 25, 2006, journal entry is read aloud.

July 25, 2006
Journal Entry

I wasn't sure I wanted to go on a family vacation to San Diego this year, but surprisingly, this trip has turned out to be an exciting experience. Today, we slept in, had a nice breakfast in the hotel restaurant, and took a carefree stroll, stopping in cool little shops along the way.

Our travels eventually led us to the site I had been waiting for: the Pacific Ocean. I've seen pictures before, but it was hard to believe it could be so enormous. I stood there just looking out in amazement as the waves gently rolled in to touch the sand, then pulled back out again. The waves moved like this over and over. The sun was shining; it glistened on the water like hundreds of shiny diamonds. If only they were real, I would bottle them up, take them home, and sell them to the highest bidder. I could be rich!

Even though the diamonds were only figments of my imagination, the ocean was really neat. As I stood with my feet in the sand, I felt the warm breeze against my skin and breathed in the smell of salt water and fish from the harbor.

There were boats of every shape and size docked at the harbor's marina. I thought about all those boats used by so many different people for so many different purposes. Some people were using boats to sail and have fun. While others, like fishermen, used their boats to earn their livings. It was fun reading the boats' names. My favorite boat, a large, white sail boat with a blue stripe along the side, was named "The Sailing Samantha."

People who live in San Diego can see the ocean all the time. They probably don't realize how lucky they are to live close to such a great place. It makes me wonder if there are things I see everyday around home that I take for granted. When we get back, I think I need to look at my surroundings in a whole new way. Maybe I'll even see a few diamonds I never noticed before.

Step
2

There are several things to keep in mind as you plan and write your journal entry. Remember, a good journal entry has the following parts:

- a date

- a description of the sights and sounds of the events or people

- a description of your feelings

- a beginning, a middle, and an end

Step
3

Use the following prompt to complete the prewriting and writing activities:

> **Think about the most important day of your life. Describe this day, or part of the day. What made this day so important? Include details so that others will know more about this memorable day.**

Step
4

Complete the graphic organizer on the next page as your prewriting activity. Use your graphic organizer to help you think through your journal entry.

Journal Entry

What day will you write about in your journal entry?

Why are you writing about this day?

Who was there?

Where did it happen?

When did it happen?

What Happened?	First:

What Happened?	Next:

What Happened?	Then:

Finally:

How did it make you and others feel?

         © 2005 Englefield & Associates, Inc.

Use the information from your graphic organizer to complete your journal entry.

Writing Activity 6

Step

5

_____

_____

_____

_____

_____

_____

_____

_____

_____

_____

_____

_____

_____

_____

_____

_____

_____

_____

_____

_____

_____

_____

_____

_____

If you need more room, continue on the next page.

Writing Activity 6

Step

5

_____

_____

_____

_____

_____

_____

_____

_____

_____

_____

_____

_____

_____

_____

_____

_____

_____

_____

_____

_____

_____

_____

Step

6

The checklist shows what your best journal entry must include. Use the checklist below to review your work.

Checklist for Writing Activity 6

☐ My journal entry has a date.

☐ I describe the most important day of my life in my journal entry.

☐ I include details about why this day is memorable.

☐ My journal entry has a beginning, middle, and end.

☐ My journal entry is well organized and complete.

☐ I try to spell words correctly.

☐ I use words that make my meaning clear. I do not use the same words over and over.

☐ I use correct punctuation and capitalization.

☐ I have written my journal entry so the reader can read my print or cursive writing.

Writing Activity 7: A Descriptive Letter

Step Follow along as the descriptive letter is read aloud.

1

March 30, 2006

Dear Rachel,

Hi, how are you? I am having a great vacation with my family! I hope that you are having a good spring break, too. My family and I are staying with my grandparents at their house on Duck Key in Florida. We flew from Columbus, Ohio, to Miami, Florida, then drove nearly two hours over the Florida Keys to get to their house.

Grandma's and Grandpa's house faces the ocean, and they have a swimming pool with a diving board and a slide. My brother and I get up every morning and have relay races in the pool. So far, I am winning the most races.

Yesterday, my grandpa and I went to the beach. We fished off the pier, swam in the ocean, made a huge sandcastle, and collected seashells for my grandma. He even let me bury him in the sand! We also grilled hot dogs for lunch and sat under a big palm tree to relax.

Tonight we are going out to a restaurant to celebrate Grandma's birthday. Grandma wants me to try the crab legs for dinner. I'm not sure I will like the taste of crab legs, but I'm sure I will enjoy a slice of Grandma's birthday cake!

We will be leaving here on Saturday. I hate to see this vacation end, but I do miss you and all of our friends. I will see you at school on Monday.

Your friend,

Anita

Step
2

There are several things to keep in mind as you plan and write your descriptive letter. Remember, a good descriptive letter has the following parts:

- a date

- a greeting

- a body that talks to the reader

- a closing

- a signature

Step
3

Use the following prompt to complete the prewriting and writing activities:

> **Write a letter to someone who is older than you. Write about what it is like growing up in your time. You might include information such as the style of clothes you wear, the music you listen to, and the types of things that interest you.**

Step
4

Complete the graphic organizer on the next page as your prewriting activity. Use your graphic organizer to help you think through your descriptive letter.

Descriptive Letter

Date:

Greeting:

Personal comment and why you are writing:

Details

First:

Second:

Third:

Fourth:

Personal comments ending the letter:

Closing:

Signature:

Use the information from your graphic organizer to complete your descriptive letter.

Writing Activity 7

Step

5

_____

_____

_____

_____

_____

_____

_____

_____

_____

_____

_____

_____

_____

_____

_____

_____

_____

_____

_____

_____

_____

If you need more room, continue on the next page.

Writing Activity 7

Step

5

_____

_____

_____

_____

_____

_____

_____

_____

_____

_____

_____

_____

_____

_____

_____

_____

_____

_____

_____

_____

_____

_____

Step

6

The checklist shows what your best descriptive letter must include. Use the checklist below to review your work.

Checklist for Writing Activity 7

☐ I use the form for a letter with a date, a greeting, a body, a closing, and a signature.

☐ My letter tells my reader why I am writing and makes personal comments.

☐ My letter describes what it's like to grow up in my time.

☐ My letter is well organized and complete.

☐ My descriptive letter includes a personal closing comment.

☐ I try to spell words correctly.

☐ I use words that make my meaning clear. I do not use the same words over and over.

☐ I use correct punctuation and capitalization.

☐ I have written my letter so the reader can read my print or cursive writing.

Writing Activity 8: A Descriptive Letter

Step Follow along as the descriptive letter is read aloud.

1

July 12, 2005

Dear Mom and Dad,

Hello, how are you? Summer camp is really cool! We are staying in a cabin with a large room that sleeps eight boys. The cabin is made of large pine logs with a tin roof. There are large screen windows on three sides of the cabin and shutters attached to each window to close if it rains. A bunk bed is placed in each corner of the room. Ryan and I are sharing a bunk. I sleep on the top bunk because Ryan is afraid that he will forget where he is sleeping and fall out of bed at night. Showers and restrooms are a short walk away.

The food here is pretty good. For every meal, the boys in every cabin take turns serving. Yesterday, it was my cabin's turn to serve breakfast. I served blueberry pancakes, Ryan dished out cups of fruit, J.P. was in charge of bacon, and Kyle poured the juice. Bill, Darius, Andre, and Levi cleared the plates from the tables and helped with the dishes.

My counselor's name is Mike, and he's very nice. He is a college junior from Missouri. He showed us how to make s'mores last night. You toast a marshmallow and place it on a piece of a chocolate bar, then sandwich the marshmallow and chocolate between graham crackers.

We have been swimming, fishing, and canoeing on the lake every day. The water was cold at first, but I got used to it. The girls from across the lake are coming over tomorrow night for a cook-out and games. We are going to play Capture the Flag. Our cabin has a plan to beat them. Can't wait to see you Sunday!

Love,

Oliver

Step 2

There are several things to keep in mind as you plan and write your descriptive letter. Remember, a good descriptive letter has the following parts:

- a date

- a greeting

- a body that talks to the reader

- a closing

- a signature

Step 3

Use the following prompt to complete the prewriting and writing activities:

> **Write a letter to a person of your choice describing your favorite place. In your letter, include why the person you are writing to would enjoy visiting your favorite place.**

Step 4

Complete the graphic organizer on the next page as your prewriting activity. Use your graphic organizer to help you think through your descriptive letter.

Descriptive Letter

Date:

Greeting:

Personal comment and why you are writing:

Details

First:

Second:

Third:

Fourth:

Personal comments ending the letter:

Closing:

Signature:

Use the information from your graphic organizer to complete your descriptive letter.

Writing Activity 8

Step

5

_____

_____

_____

_____

_____

_____

_____

_____

_____

_____

_____

_____

_____

_____

_____

_____

_____

_____

_____

_____

_____

_____

_____

If you need more room, continue on the next page.

Writing Activity 8

Step

5

_____

_____

_____

_____

_____

_____

_____

_____

_____

_____

_____

_____

_____

_____

_____

_____

_____

_____

_____

_____

_____

_____

Step

6

The checklist shows what your best descriptive letter must include. Use the checklist below to review your work.

Checklist for Writing Activity 8

☐ I use the form for a letter with a date, a greeting, a body, a closing, and a signature.

☐ My letter tells my reader why I am writing and makes personal comments.

☐ My letter describes my favorite place.

☐ I include why the person I am writing to would like to visit my favorite place.

☐ My descriptive letter includes a personal closing comment.

☐ I try to spell words correctly.

☐ I use words that make my meaning clear. I do not use the same words over and over.

☐ I use correct punctuation and capitalization.

☐ I have written my story so the reader can read my print or cursive writing.

© 2005 Englefield & Associates, Inc.

3 The Direction Communication Process

(Directions and Invitation)

What is the Direction Communication Process?

The purpose of the direction communication process is to tell someone how to make something or do something. Two examples of the direction communication process are directions and an invitation.

Directions contain written information in step-by-step order. Directions tell how to make something or how to do something, and they should be easy for the reader to follow.

An **invitation** is a short note or letter that invites someone to an event such as a birthday party. Invitations include information such as the type of event, the location of the event, the time and date of the event, and RSVP details. Invitations should contain all the details invited guests need to know in order to attend the event.

Features of Directions
- Directions are given in correct order.
- Directions tell someone how to do something or how to make something.
- Directions should be easy to follow and understand.

Words that Provide Directions
- Direction words: right, left, north, south, east, west
- Prepositions: in, on, under, before, after
- Phrases: when you see the…; before you reach the…; after you pass the…
- Direction verbs: mix, blend, stir, insert, pour

Features of an Invitation
- An invitation invites someone to an event.
- An invitation tells who is invited and who is hosting the event.
- An invitation indicates the type of event.
- An invitation indicates the time and date of the event, as well as RSVP details.
- An invitation indicates where the event will take place and often includes a map to the location.

Writing Activity 9: Directions
(How to Do Something)

Step

1

Follow along as the directions "How to Make a Banana Split" are read aloud.

How to Make a Banana Split

A banana split is a great dessert that's easy to make. Banana splits require the following ingredients: bananas, ice cream, hot fudge or chocolate sauce, whipped cream, chopped peanuts, and cherries. You will also need boat-shaped dishes, an ice cream spoon, a dull knife, and serving spoons.

1. The first and most important ingredient in a banana split is the banana. Start by peeling a banana. Then, using a dull knife, carefully slice the banana lengthwise so you have two canoe-shaped slices.

2. Place the banana slices in a boat-shaped dish or any dish that is long enough to hold the slices. If you don't have a long dish, cut each banana slice in half and place all four pieces in a bowl.

3   Next, you will need your ice cream. Most people prefer vanilla ice cream on their banana splits, but you can serve any flavor you like. Scoop out two spoonfuls of ice cream and place them side-by-side on your bananas.

4. Now it is time for the hot fudge or chocolate sauce. Pour as much as you would like all over the banana slices and scoops of ice cream.

5. At this time, sprinkle three spoonfuls of peanuts onto the banana split. If you have any other favorite toppings you would like to enjoy on your dessert, add them now.

6. Finally, put some whipped cream on each scoop of ice cream, and top off your delicious banana split with two cherries. Serve the banana split to a friend, or enjoy this wonderful dessert by yourself.

       © 2005 Englefield & Associates, Inc.

Step
2

There are several things to keep in mind as you plan and write your directions. Remember, good directions have the following parts:

- a beginning that tells what the directions will explain how to do

- a description of what materials are needed to complete the task

- steps that are given in order (directions may be written line by line or in paragraph form)

- a starting and an ending point

- an opening statement and a concluding sentence

Step
3

Use the following prompt to complete the prewriting and writing activities:

> **A friend has asked you how to make your favorite food. Write a set of directions to make your favorite food so your friend can follow them easily. Once your directions are written, have your friend follow them exactly.**

Step
4

Complete the graphic organizer on the next page as your prewriting activity. Use your graphic organizer to help you think through your directions.

Directions

How to Do Something

How to: _____

What is needed to begin:

Step 1:

Step 2:

Step 3:

Step 4:

Step 5:

Finally:

Use the information from your graphic organizer to complete your directions.

Writing Activity 9

Step

5

If you need more room, continue on the next page.

Writing Activity 9

Step

5

_____

_____

_____

_____

_____

_____

_____

_____

_____

_____

_____

_____

_____

_____

_____

_____

_____

_____

_____

_____

_____

_____

_____

_____

_____

_____

Step

6

The checklist shows what your best directions must include. Use the checklist below to review your work.

Checklist for Writing Activity 9

☐ My directions begin with a sentence telling what my directions will explain how to do.

☐ My directions clearly describe the materials that are needed to make my favorite food.

☐ My directions use the correct order to tell my friend what to do first, next, and so on to make my favorite food.

☐ My directions have a concluding sentence describing my favorite food.

☐ My directions are well organized and complete.

☐ I try to spell words correctly.

☐ I use words that make my meaning clear. I do not use the same words over and over.

☐ I use correct punctuation and capitalization.

☐ I have written my directions so the reader can read my print or cursive writing.

Writing Activity 10: Directions
(How to Go Somewhere)

Step 1   Look at the map below. Follow along as the set of directions for traveling from the Food Court to the Theater Parking Lot is read aloud.

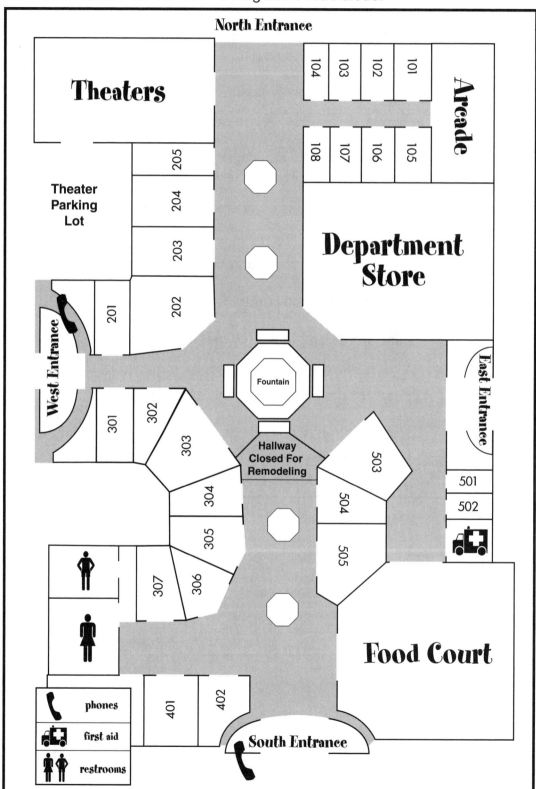

Step 1

Directions for Traveling from the Food Court to the Theater Parking Lot:

You are located in the Food Court in the southeast corner of the mall. You are trying to get to the Theater Parking Lot found south of the Theaters.

1. Exit the Food Court to the north until you see the East Entrance of the mall.

2. Walk west toward the fountain.

3. Travel around the fountain in the northwest direction. Do not pass the North Entrance mall hallway.

4. Head toward the North Entrance. You will see the Theaters at the end of the hall, on the west side.

5. Go through the Theaters toward the southern exit.

You have made it to the Theater Parking Lot.

Step
2

There are several things to keep in mind as you plan and write your own directions. Remember, good directions have the following parts:

- a beginning that tells where the directions begin and end

- a description of what is needed to complete the task

- steps that are given in order

- a starting point and an ending point

Step
3

Use the following prompt to complete the prewriting and writing activities:

> **You and a good friend are playing "Monster Man" at the Arcade. You look at your watch and realize the movie you planned to see has already started. Your friend volunteers to call his parents and let them know you need to be picked up early. You remember seeing a sign that says the phones at the West Entrance are out of order. Using the map of the mall on page 60, give directions to your friend on how to get to the phones at the South Entrance of the mall.**

Step
4

Complete the graphic organizer on the next page as your prewriting activity. Use your graphic organizer to help you think through your directions.

Directions

How to Go Somewhere

Where are you going? _____

Where to start:

First:

Second:

Third:

Fourth:

Fifth:

Where you finish:

Use the information from your graphic organizer to complete your directions.

Writing Activity 10

Step

5

_____

_____

_____

_____

_____

_____

_____

_____

_____

_____

_____

_____

_____

_____

_____

_____

_____

_____

_____

_____

If you need more room, continue on the next page.

Writing Activity 10

Step

5

Step

6

The checklist shows what your best directions must include. Use the checklist below to review your work.

Checklist for Writing Activity 10

☐ My directions start with a sentence telling where my directions begin and end.

☐ My directions use step-by-step order (1, 2, 3, 4, …) to tell my friend what to do first, next, and so on in order to walk from the Arcade to the phone booth at the South Entrance.

☐ My directions give accurate details and directions.

☐ My directions include a concluding sentence.

☐ My directions are well organized and complete.

☐ I try to spell words correctly.

☐ I use words that make my meaning clear. I do not use the same words over and over.

☐ I use correct punctuation and capitalization.

☐ I have written my directions so the reader can read my print or cursive writing.

       © 2005 Englefield & Associates, Inc.

Writing Activity 11: Invitation

Step
1
Follow along as the invitation below is read aloud.

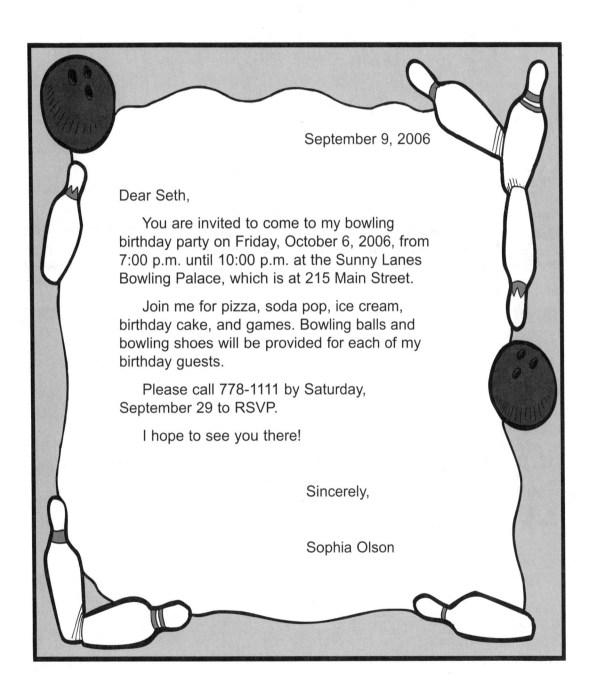

September 9, 2006

Dear Seth,

You are invited to come to my bowling birthday party on Friday, October 6, 2006, from 7:00 p.m. until 10:00 p.m. at the Sunny Lanes Bowling Palace, which is at 215 Main Street.

Join me for pizza, soda pop, ice cream, birthday cake, and games. Bowling balls and bowling shoes will be provided for each of my birthday guests.

Please call 778-1111 by Saturday, September 29 to RSVP.

I hope to see you there!

Sincerely,

Sophia Olson

Step

2

There are several things to keep in mind as you plan and write your invitation. Remember, a good invitation has the following parts:

- information about where and when to attend

- the type of event or the purpose of the event

- information for an RSVP

- important details about the event

Step

3

Use the following prompt to complete the prewriting and writing activities:

> **Write an invitation to parents of students in your class. Invite the parents to participate in your school's career day. Ask them to come and present information about their careers to the members of your class.**

Step

4

Complete the graphic organizer on the next page as your prewriting activity. Use your graphic organizer to help you think through your invitation.

Invitation

What is the invitation for?

Who is writing the invitation?

Who is being invited?

Where? (location)

When? (date and time)

Other important information:

R.S.V.P. (who and when)

Use the information from your graphic organizer to complete your invitation.

Writing Activity 11

Step

5

_____

_____

_____

_____

_____

_____

_____

_____

_____

_____

_____

_____

_____

_____

_____

_____

_____

_____

_____

_____

If you need more room, continue on the next page.

Writing Activity 11

Step

5

_____

_____

_____

_____

_____

_____

_____

_____

_____

_____

_____

_____

_____

_____

_____

_____

_____

_____

_____

_____

_____

_____

_____

Step

6

The checklist shows what your best invitation must include. Use the checklist below to review your work.

Checklist for Writing Activity 11

☐ My invitation includes all the important details for my guests such as the type of event, where and when to attend, and RSVP information.

☐ I let my guests know why I am inviting them.

☐ I try to spell words correctly without using any help.

☐ I use interesting words.

☐ My sentences and proper names begin with a capital letter.

☐ My sentences end with a period, an exclamation point, or a question mark.

☐ I have written my invitation so the reader can read my print or cursive writing.

Writing Activity 12: Invitation

Step
1 Follow along as the invitation below is read aloud.

August 2, 2007

Dear Rocket Soccer Player,

    The end of the season is coming soon! In order to celebrate the great season we had this summer, I would like to invite you and your family to an end of the season cookout and pool party on Friday, August 20, 2007. Please come around 1:30 p.m. You are welcome to stay as long as you would like.

    Awards for the season will be given at 2:30 p.m. There will be hot dogs and hamburgers on the grill, as well as pasta salad, chips, and soda pop. Don't forget your bathing suit and towel for swimming after the awards.

    The party will be held at my house at 1222 Eastgate Drive. To RSVP, please call me at 987-2222 before August 15, 2007.

Sincerely,

Coach Baker

Step
2
There are several things to keep in mind as you plan and write your invitation. Remember, a good invitation has the following parts:

- information about where and when to attend

- the type of event or the purpose of the event

- information for an RSVP

- important details about the event

Step
3
Use the following prompt to complete the prewriting and writing activities:

Write an invitation to your friends inviting them to a picnic to celebrate the end of the school year.

Step
4
Complete the graphic organizer on the next page as your prewriting activity. Use your graphic organizer to help you think through your invitation.

Invitation

What is the invitation for?

Who is writing the invitation?

Who is being invited?

Where? (location)

When? (date and time)

Other important information:

R.S.V.P. (who and when)

Use the information from your graphic organizer to complete your invitation.

Writing Activity 12

Step

5

_____

_____

_____

_____

_____

_____

_____

_____

_____

_____

_____

_____

_____

_____

_____

_____

_____

_____

_____

_____

_____

If you need more room, continue on the next page.

Writing Activity 12

Step

5

_____

_____

_____

_____

_____

_____

_____

_____

_____

_____

_____

_____

_____

_____

_____

_____

_____

_____

_____

_____

_____

_____

Step 6

The checklist shows what your best invitation must include. Use the checklist below to review your work.

Checklist for Writing Activity 12

☐ My invitation includes all the important details for my guests such as the type of event, where and when to attend, and RSVP information.

☐ I let my guests know why I am inviting them.

☐ I try to spell words correctly without using any help.

☐ I use interesting words.

☐ My sentences and proper names begin with a capital letter.

☐ My sentences end with a period, an exclamation point, or a question mark.

☐ I have written my invitation so the reader can read my print or cursive writing.

© 2005 Englefield & Associates, Inc.

The Explanation Communication Process

(Thank-You Note, Summary, and Informational Report)

What is the Explanation Communication Process?

Writers use the explanation communication process when they want readers to understand something. An explanation explains something using facts or details. Three examples of the explanation communication process are: a thank-you note, a summary, and an informational report.

A **thank-you note** is a short note thanking someone for something that was given to you or done for you. A thank-you note is written in the form of a letter; it includes a greeting, a body, and a closing.

A **summary** is a short version of a story. A summary lists only the main ideas and major points; it does not contain supporting details. A summary should be written in your own words.

An **informational report** contains facts. Reports can be written on real people, places, things, or events. An informational report is nonfiction.

Features of the Thank-You Note

- Thank-you notes are written in letter form.

- A thank-you note explains why you are thankful for something done for you or given to you.

Features of a Summary (Only the Important Information)

- A summary tells only about the main idea and important information.

- Summaries do not include supporting details or repeated information.

- A summary is shorter in length than the original version of the story.

Features of an Informational Report

- An informational report is nonfiction writing about a person, place, thing, or event.

- An informational report provides information about some or all of the following questions:

  What or who is it?   Where is it?   When is it?

  What does it look like?   What does it do?   Why is it important?

Writing Activity 13: Informational Report

Step

1

Follow along as the informational report "The First Surfers" is read aloud.

The First Surfers

Although no one can be absolutely sure about the origins of surfing, as early as the twelfth century, surfers carved pictures of their traditions into Hawaiian lava rock.

The origin of surfing is deeply rooted in the ancient Hawaiian system of laws, which favored royalty over commoners in the kingdom. Hawaiians referred to surfing as "he'enalu" or wave sliding. He'enalu was a noble and exclusive occupation for kings and queens. Chiefs used wave sliding and other sports to show their strength and command over their people. The great skill the royal surfers displayed led people to believe the surf riders were supreme over both water and land.

Although surfing was very important to the Hawaiian culture in the late 1700s, the sport was deeply affected by the arrival of Europeans and Americans who came first as explorers and traders and later as missionaries and settlers. Missionaries described surfing as dangerous, disorganized, terrifying, and confusing. Declaring the sport a waste of time, they preached against surfing and introduced Hawaiians to new forms of recreation. By 1890, surfing in Hawaii was nearly extinct. If not for the dedication of a few kings, surfing may not have survived.

By the early 1900s, the missionaries' influence in Hawaii began to decline. In 1905, a teenager named Duke Kahanamoku, who spent most of his days surfing, formed a surf club with his friends, "The Club of Waves." Duke's club was credited with getting Hawaiians excited about surfing again.

The popularity of surfing eventually made its way to the California coast in the 1950s. The waves along the shoreline, the introduction of lighter weight surfboards made of polyester foam or fiberglass, teen surf movies, beach parties, and popular music all helped to renew people's interest in surfing. Surfing remains a popular sport today, particularly in Hawaii, California, and Australia.

Step
2

There are several things to keep in mind as you plan and write your own informational report. Remember, a good informational report includes the following parts:

- a title

- an explanation of the topic

- only the important information

- a summary of what I have learned

Step
3

Use the following prompt to complete the prewriting and writing activities:

Read through the information given about tornadoes on the next page. Use the Information Planning Guide to select and group the information you will use to create a report that provides the reader with information about tornadoes. Use the information you gather in the planning guide to complete your graphic organizer. You do not have to use every fact to complete your report. You will need to organize the material and add words of your own.

Write a report on tornadoes. Use the facts given in "Tornado Facts and Safety" along with other facts you know. Use the informational report organizer to write an introduction, a body of one to three paragraphs, and a summary that ends your report.

Step

3

Tornado Facts & Safety

- Crouch down and cover your head.

- The largest tornadoes, classified as F4 or F5, can be more than one mile wide, last up to an hour or more, and travel over paths averaging 30-35 miles long.

- If you are outside during a tornado, go to the basement of a nearby building or lie flat in a ditch.

- The rotating winds of tornadoes may range from about 40 miles per hour to more than 300 miles per hour.

- A tornado often looks like a funnel with the fat part at the top.

- The Fujita Scale, developed by Theodore Fujita, a University of Chicago scientist, is used to classify tornadoes.

- A tornado watch means a tornado is possible.

- If you are in a car or mobile home, get out and head for safety.

- Tornadoes can occur in most parts of the world, except in polar regions.

- Meteorologists can predict possible severe weather 12 to 48 hours in advance.

- If there is a tornado warning, go inside to a safe place to protect yourself from flying glass or debris.

- Tornadoes are sometimes called "twisters."

- F0 and F1 tornadoes are the smallest and weakest.

- A tornado is a violent column of air extending from a thunderstorm to the ground.

- Tornadoes can be various sizes, shapes, and colors.

- The Red Cross suggests you assemble a disaster supplies kit that includes a first aid kit, a battery powered radio, a flashlight and extra batteries, bottled water, nonperishable food, a can opener, sturdy shoes, work gloves, and instructions on how to turn off home utilities.

- A tornado warning means a tornado has been spotted.

- Tornadoes most often hit the midwestern and southern United States during the spring and summer months.

- After a tornado, watch out for fallen power lines.

- Tornadoes are classified by wind speed and damage, according to the Fujita Scale.

- The National Weather Service is locating Doppler radars across the country to detect air movement.

- Signs of a tornado may include: a greenish-black color to the sky, falling hail, the sound of a railroad train, and a funnel shaped cloud.

- Never use candles during a tornado.

- Go to interior rooms or halls on the lowest floor.

- Before a tornado, purchase a weather radio with a warning alarm tone and battery back-up to receive warnings.

Step 4 Complete the informational report planning guide and graphic organizer as your prewriting activities. Use your planning guide and graphic organizer to help you think through your informational report.

Information Planning Guide

Topic:

Planning Questions	Key Words – Short Notes
What are they?	
What do they do?	
What do they look like?	
Where do they live?	
Why are they important?	
Summary: What are the most important things you have learned about this topic?	

Informational Report

Title: _____

INTRODUCTION (What is the report about?)

Paragraph 1:

Paragraph 2:

Paragraph 3:

SUMMARY (The most important points you want to make)

Use the information from your graphic organizer to complete your informational report.

Writing Activity 13

Step

5

_____

_____

_____

_____

_____

_____

_____

_____

_____

_____

_____

_____

_____

_____

_____

_____

_____

_____

_____

_____

If you need more room, continue on the next page.

Writing Activity 13

Step

5

       © 2005 Englefield & Associates, Inc.

Step

6

The checklist shows what your best informational report must include. Use the checklist below to review your work.

Checklist for Writing Activity 13

☐ My informational report has a title.

☐ My informational report tells the reader the topic of my report.

☐ My report includes only points that are important for readers to know.

☐ My report does not include information that is not important to making my main points.

☐ My report tells the reader what I have learned.

☐ My report has a beginning, middle, and end.

☐ I try to spell words correctly without using any help.

☐ I use interesting words.

☐ My sentences and proper names begin with a capital letter.

☐ My sentences end with a period, an exclamation point, or a question mark.

☐ I have written my report so the reader can read my print or cursive writing.

Writing Activity 14: Informational Report

Step

1

Follow along as the informational report "Archaeologists" is read aloud.

Archaeologists

Archaeologists are scientists who study the behavior and culture of human beings from the past. They study human societies that existed hundreds, thousands, or millions of years ago. You probably know about some places and people of ancient societies like the Parthenon of the Greeks or the pyramids of the Egyptians because of the work of archaeologists.

Most of the information these scientists gather comes from studying objects lying on or under the ground. They examine the remains of societies from the past such as fossils or preserved bones of people and animals, food remains, building ruins and human artifacts. Human artifacts are the tools the people of the past society used, the pottery they made and used as well as the jewelry they wore. Archaeologists study the changes in past societies over time.

Archaeologists use a variety of tools. Bulldozers are used to remove large layers of soil from the top of the excavation site that doesn't contain artifacts or remains. Picks and shovels are used to remove smaller areas of soil. Trowels and hand adzes are used for careful excavation around buried materials. When they discover fragile items like skeletal remains, they use dental picks and brushes to delicately clean them without damaging them.

Archaeologists have three major goals. They try to determine chronology. This means they try to determine the time a particular society lived in history. Next, they do their best to reconstruct what life might have been like for the people of that society. They try to reconstruct a society by using physical remains to create a picture of the past. Their third goal is to explain what happened in the past. They try to answer questions like why a society collapsed and disappeared.

In summary, archaeologists study the past to learn about things that could help the people today. Through their work we can compare societies and determine how they are alike and different. For example, past societies developed water and sewer systems that are the basis for ours today. The present is built on the knowledge of the past.

Step
2

There are several things to keep in mind as you plan and write your own informational report. Remember, a good informational report includes the following parts:

- a title

- an explanation of the topic

- only the important information

- a summary of what I have learned

Step
3

Use the following prompt to complete the prewriting and writing activities:

> **Read through the information given about audiologists on the next page. Use the Information Planning Guide to select and group the information you will use to create a report that provides the reader with information about audiologists. Use the information you gather in the planning guide to complete your graphic organizer. You do not have to use every fact to complete your report. You will need to organize the material and add words of your own.**
>
> **Write a report on audiologists. Use the facts given in "Facts About Audiologists" along with other facts you know. Use the informational report organizer to write an introduction, a body of one to three paragraphs, and a summary that ends your report.**

Step

3

Facts about Audiologists

- how much of a hearing loss an individual has is determined by an audiologist

- audiologists use devices to test a person's hearing and determine if they have a hearing loss

- audiologists refer patients to surgeons if an operation is needed

- audiologists need to be good at communicating information to their patients

- audiologists can help people with balance problems caused by problems with their inner ear

- audiologists work with people who have hearing problems

- audiologists interpret results of the tests they give

- audiologists can test the hearing of workers who work in places that are noisy, industrial settings that can cause hearing loss

- audiologists decide which hearing aid will work best

- audiologists work with children who are born with a hearing loss

- audiologists work with doctors to diagnose the problem and provide treatment

- some audiologists sell hearing aids

- audiologists help older people with hearing losses

- audiologists help deaf people figure out what devices they might need to have in their home, school, or work setting like a light that would tell them the fire alarm went off

- audiologists can teach at universities and medical schools

- audiologists make ear molds so the hearing aid will fit and work well

- audiologists work with speech language pathologists to talk with them about how the hearing loss will effect the patient's speaking and communication abilities

- audiologists work with people of all ages

- audiologists work with educators to give them suggestions about what they can do to help deaf or hearing impaired children in their classroom learn

Step
4

Complete the informational report planning guide and graphic organizer as your prewriting activities. Use your planning guide and graphic organizer to help you think through your informational report.

Information Planning Guide

Topic:

Planning Questions	Key Words – Short Notes
What are they?	
What do they do?	
What do they look like?	
Where do they live?	
Why are they important?	
Summary: What are the most important things you have learned about this topic?	

Informational Report

Title: _____

INTRODUCTION (What is the report about?)

Paragraph 1:

Paragraph 2:

Paragraph 3:

SUMMARY (The most important points you want to make)

Use the information from your graphic organizer to complete your informational report.

Writing Activity 14

Step

5

_____

_____

_____

_____

_____

_____

_____

_____

_____

_____

_____

_____

_____

_____

_____

_____

_____

_____

_____

_____

_____

If you need more room, continue on the next page.

Writing Activity 14

Step

5

Step

6

The checklist shows what your best informational report must include. Use the checklist below to review your work.

Checklist for Writing Activity 14

☐ My informational report has a title.

☐ My informational report tells the reader the topic of my report.

☐ My report includes only points that are important for readers to know.

☐ My report does not include information that is not important to making my main points.

☐ My report tells the reader what I have learned.

☐ My report has a beginning, middle, and end.

☐ I try to spell words correctly without using any help.

☐ I use interesting words.

☐ My sentences and proper names begin with a capital letter.

☐ My sentences end with a period, an exclamation point, or a question mark.

☐ I have written my report so the reader can read my print or cursive writing.

Writing Activity 15: Informational Report

Step 1 Follow along as the informational report "Cesar Estrada Chavez" is read aloud.

Cesar Estrada Chavez

Cesar Estrada Chavez, the grandson of Mexican immigrants, was born March 31, 1927, near Yuma, Arizona. In the late 1930s, Cesar and his family moved to California where they became part of the migrant community that traveled from farm to farm, community to community, picking fruits and vegetables during harvest times. Living conditions were poor for the farm workers; the days were long and the pay was small. The Chavez family often found themselves sleeping in their car.

Once Cesar completed the eighth grade, he quit school and worked full-time in the vineyards. Cesar joined the Navy in 1944 and served for two years, fighting in World War II. After completing his military duty, he moved back to California and returned to work in the fields. Cesar began to see a need for change. In 1948, he took part in an unsuccessful strike to protest low wages and poor working conditions. By 1952, Cesar was traveling throughout California, making speeches in support of farm workers' rights and urging Mexican-Americans to register to vote.

Cesar led a successful strike of California grape-pickers in 1965 that lasted for five years. The striking workers demanded higher wages and encouraged Americans to boycott grapes. The strike attracted national attention, and for the first time, increased public awareness of the terrible conditions farm workers faced. Chavez was able to rally millions of supporters for the farm workers' cause.

Throughout his lifetime, Cesar continued to fight for farm workers' rights. He also fought against the use of toxic pesticides on grapes and other produce. Cesar advocated nonviolent protest and became well respected throughout the country. Cesar E. Chavez died on April 23, 1993, but his legacy of establishing farm workers' rights continues today.

Step 2

There are several things to keep in mind as you plan and write your own informational report. Remember, a good informational report includes the following parts:

- a title

- an explanation of the topic

- only the important information

- a summary of what I have learned

Step 3

Use the following prompt to complete the prewriting and writing activities:

> **Read through the information given about the Underground Railroad on the next page. Use the Information Planning Guide to select and group the information you will use to create a report that provides the reader with information about the Underground Railroad. Use the information you gather in the planning guide to complete your graphic organizer. You do not have to use every fact to complete your report. You will need to organize the material and add words of your own.**
>
> **Write a report on the Underground Railroad. Use the facts given in "Facts About the Underground Railroad" along with other facts you know. Use the informational report organizer to write an introduction, a body of one to three paragraphs, and a summary that ends your report.**

Step

3

Facts About the Underground Railroad

- The Underground Railroad wasn't a railroad at all.
- The Underground Railroad was a network of anti-slavery Northerners who provided food, shelter, and a safe place for slaves seeking freedom.
- The purpose of the Underground Railroad was to help slaves reach safety in free states or in Canada.
- Runaway slaves used the North Star to guide their way.
- Slaves who escaped looked for "stations" in towns where free blacks and others would help hide them.
- "Conductors" met runaways at border points, such as Cincinnati, Ohio.
- Harriet Tubman was a famous "conductor" who was nicknamed "Moses."
- The runaways faced dangers of being captured by bloodhounds or patrollers.
- Handbills would often advertise the escape of a slave.
- Runaways would travel at night, often following rivers and staying off roads.
- Some historians believe the Underground Railroad helped make people aware of the evils of slavery.
- "A friend with friends" was a password used by conductors.
- With the passage of the Fugitive Slave Law of 1850, runaway slaves were not safe in northern cities. The law stated that a person could be fined or imprisoned for not helping a federal marshal arrest a runaway.
- The Society of Friends, or Quakers, actively fought for the rights of runaways.
- A lantern on a hitching post would signal a "safe house."
- A good friend of Harriet Tubman was the Quaker businessman Thomas Garrett. Garrett worked the Underground Railroad for over 40 years.
- The routes to freedom were often over 500 hundred miles long.
- For some runaways, the journey to Canada took from two months to one year.
- Often, runaways would be forced to hide in wood boxes, secret passageways, or even specially designed cupboards.
- In 1865, slavery was abolished with the 13th Amendment to the United States Constitution.

Step

4

Complete the informational report planning guide and graphic organizer as your prewriting activities. Use your planning guide and graphic organizer to help you think through your informational report.

Information Planning Guide

Topic:

Planning Questions	Key Words – Short Notes
What are they?	
What do they do?	
What do they look like?	
Where do they live?	
Why are they important?	
Summary: What are the most important things you have learned about this topic?	

Informational Report

Title: _____

INTRODUCTION (What is the report about?)

Paragraph 1:

Paragraph 2:

Paragraph 3:

SUMMARY (The most important points you want to make)

Use the information from your graphic organizer to complete your informational report.

Writing Activity 15

Step

5

_____

_____

_____

_____

_____

_____

_____

_____

_____

_____

_____

_____

_____

_____

_____

_____

_____

_____

_____

_____

_____

If you need more room, continue on the next page.

Writing Activity 15

Step

5

_____

_____

_____

_____

_____

_____

_____

_____

_____

_____

_____

_____

_____

_____

_____

_____

_____

_____

_____

_____

_____

_____

_____

Step
6

The checklist shows what your best informational report must include. Use the checklist below to review your work.

Checklist for Writing Activity 15

☐ My informational report has a title.

☐ My informational report tells the reader the topic of my report.

☐ My report includes only points that are important for readers to know.

☐ My report does not include information that is not important to making my main points.

☐ My report tells the reader what I have learned.

☐ My report has a beginning, middle, and end.

☐ I try to spell words correctly without using any help.

☐ I use interesting words.

☐ My sentences and proper names begin with a capital letter.

☐ My sentences end with a period, an exclamation point, or a question mark.

☐ I have written my report so the reader can read my print or cursive writing.

Writing Activity 16: Summary

Step 1 Follow along as two passages are read. The first passage is a report called "The New Golden Dollar." The second passage is a summary of "The New Golden Dollar."

The New Golden Dollar

Many Americans wonder what the story is behind the new Golden Dollar. In the early 1990s, the demand for dollar coins surged as the vending machine industry began to recognize the benefits of dollar coins. This increased demand began to exhaust the government's supply of Susan B. Anthony one-dollar coins.

On December 1, 1997, President Bill Clinton signed into law the "United States Dollar Coin Act of 1997," requiring the U.S. Treasury Department to place into circulation a new one-dollar coin. The new Golden Dollar would replace the Susan B. Anthony coin that had been in circulation since 1979. According to the Coin Act, the new dollar coin had to meet several requirements. The coin had to be gold in color and have the same diameter as the Susan B. Anthony coin: 26.5 millimeters. Its edge needed to be smooth. The coin had to have metallic, anti-counterfeiting properties similar to other U.S. coins. The obverse side of the new coin had to show one or more women; the coin could not picture a living person. The reverse side had to display an eagle.

Once the requirements were issued, the next step was deciding who would be featured on the obverse side of the coin. In April 1998, the Dollar Coin Design Advisory Committee was formed. The committee met in open session and took suggestions from the public. Ideas for the coin's design came by mail and e-mail, through faxes, and phone messages.

On June 9, 1998, the design committee recommended the new Golden Dollar coin feature Sacajawea, the Native American woman who assisted Lewis and Clark on their expedition from the Northern Great Plains to the Pacific Ocean. Once the recommendation was accepted, the U.S. Mint contacted individuals and organizations to submit coin designs. Almost one year and 121 designs later, the final design for the Golden Dollar was revealed on May 4, 1999. Full-scale production of Golden Dollar coins featuring Sacajawea began in November 1999. The coins started to appear in circulation two months later, in January 2000.

Step
1

Summary of "The New Golden Dollar"

When the vending machine industry began to see the benefits of one-dollar coins, the government's supply of Susan B. Anthony coins decreased. This led to President Clinton signing the "United States Dollar Coin Act of 1997." The act required the Treasury Department to put a new one-dollar coin into circulation. The coin had to be designed with specific features of size, color, and anti-counterfeiting properties. The back of the coin had to picture an eagle. The other side had to show one or more women who are no longer living.

The Dollar Coin Advisory Committee took suggestions from the public about the new coin's design. It was decided that the new coin would feature Sacajawea, the Native American who helped Lewis and Clark, explorers of the Northwestern United States. Production of the Golden Dollar began in November 1999, and the new coins were put into circulation in January 2000.

Step

2

There are several things to keep in mind as you plan to write a summary. Remember, a good summary:

- includes the main ideas

- eliminates unimportant or unnecessary information

- does not include many details

- is written in your own words

Step

3

Use the following prompt to complete the prewriting and writing activities:

> **Read the passage "April Fool's Day" on page 107 and write a summary.**

Step

4

Complete the graphic organizer on page 108 as your prewriting activity. Use your graphic organizer to help you think through your summary of "April Fool's Day."

Step

3

April Fool's Day

Have you ever wondered where the tradition of playing silly pranks on April 1 began? Believe it or not, this holiday has been around for a long time. In France, during the early sixteenth century, the start of the new year was observed in early spring on April 1. To observe the holiday, the French danced and celebrated with festivities lasting late into the night, similar to the way people today celebrate New Year's Eve on December 31.

In the late 1500s, the Gregorian Calendar was introduced by King Charles IX of France. The new calendar moved New Year's Day to January 1. In those days, however, communication was poor. Most information was relayed by people traveling on foot. Thus, some of the French did not receive word of the calendar change until years after New Year's Day had been moved. These people, along with some of Charles's subjects who refused to celebrate January 1, continued to observe New Year's Day on April 1 and became known as "April fools." The fools were subject to pranks, ridicule, and practical jokes. The fools were given the name "Poisson d'Avril" meaning April fish, because at that time of the year, the sun was in the zodiac sign of Pisces, the fish.

The tradition of harassing and teasing people on April 1 continued long after January 1 became widely accepted as New Year's Day by the general population of France. French children would often put paper fish on their friends' backs and yell "Poisson d'Avril." The practice of playing small pranks on April 1 eventually spread to other European countries, including England and Scotland. By the eighteenth century, April Fool's Day had made its way to the American colonies of both England and France. April 1 became an international day for fun and jest.

April Fool's Day is a holiday that is still celebrated today. The small tricks people play are intended to be funny but never hurtful. Whenever a prankster successfully pulls off a trick, he or she yells, "April Fools!" The next time you fall for, or play, an April Fool's joke, think of the Poisson d'Avril who mistakenly observed April 1 as the first day of the new year in sixteenth century France.

Steps for Writing a Summary

Only the Main Ideas

Topic: _____

Complete the Following Steps:

Step 1 ☐ **Skim the reading selection and begin to look for the main idea.**

Step 2 ☐ **Underline the topic sentence for each paragraph in the text selection.** (If there is no topic sentence, write one for the paragraph.)

Step 3 ☐ **Cross out unimportant information in the text selection.**

Step 4 ☐ **Cross out information that is repeated.**

Step 5 ☐ **Write what the text selection is about. Include only important information.**

Use the information from your graphic organizer to complete your summary.

Writing Activity 16

Step

5

_____

_____

_____

_____

_____

_____

_____

_____

_____

_____

_____

_____

_____

_____

_____

_____

_____

_____

_____

_____

_____

_____

_____

_____

_____

If you need more room, continue on the next page.

Writing Activity 16

Step

5

_____

_____

_____

_____

_____

_____

_____

_____

_____

_____

_____

_____

_____

_____

_____

_____

_____

_____

_____

_____

_____

_____

_____

       © 2005 Englefield & Associates, Inc.

Step
6

The checklist shows what your best summary must include. Use the checklist below to review your work.

Checklist for Writing Activity 16

☐ My summary has a sentence that identifies the topic of the text selection.

☐ My summary states the main ideas of the text selection.

☐ My summary does not include information that is not important to the story.

☐ My summary has an ending.

☐ I try to spell words correctly without using any help.

☐ I use interesting words.

☐ My sentences and proper names begin with a capital letter.

☐ My sentences end with a period, an exclamation point, or a question mark.

☐ I have written my summary so the reader can read my print or cursive writing.

Writing Activity 17: Summary

Step
1

Follow along as two passages are read. The first passage is a narrative called "My Big Game." The second passage is a summary of "My Big Game."

My Big Game

It was the last game of the season and my team, the Bobcats, was undefeated. We were playing the Hornets, the best team in the league. They were also undefeated. The game was tied 3-3 at the bottom of the ninth inning.

I knew I was the next person up to bat. I was beginning to feel knots twist the inside of my stomach. It's an honor for Coach to trust me enough to bat at a time like this, I thought. I didn't want to let him or my team down.

I watched my teammate, Jeff, who was up at the plate. The sun hit his face, and I thought he looked confident. When the umpire yelled, "Strike!" for the third time, my stomach dropped. The pressure was all on me. It was the bottom of the ninth inning, and we had two outs. I took a deep breath and tried to look calm as I stepped up to the plate. The first pitch went wide; the second was a strike.

I felt myself become more nervous and took another deep breath to refocus. When the next pitch was thrown, I swung as hard as I could. I felt the ball make contact with my bat. "SNAP!" I threw my bat and headed for first base.

I was running as fast as my legs could carry me when I saw my coach jumping up and down and cheering from the sidelines. I looked toward the outfield and saw the ball fall over the fence. I had hit a home run! I ran around the diamond, touching first, second, and third base. As I approached home plate, I was greeted by my coach and my entire team! They lifted me onto their shoulders as everyone cheered. The day of the big game was the best day of my life!

         © 2005 Englefield & Associates, Inc.

Step
1

Summary of "My Big Game"

Two undefeated baseball teams, the Bobcats and the Hornets, were playing their last game of the season. The game was tied 3 to 3 at the bottom of the ninth inning. After a teammate struck out, the narrator of the story was up to bat, and his team already had two outs. On the third pitch, despite his being nervous, the narrator hit the ball as hard as he could. As he ran the bases, he looked up and saw the ball drop over the fence. He had scored a home run to win the game! The coach and team cheered for the batter as he approached home plate. They lifted the narrator onto their shoulders in celebration. The day of the big game was the best day of the narrator's life.

Step

2

There are several things to keep in mind as you plan to write a summary. Remember, a good summary:

- includes the main ideas

- eliminates unimportant or unnecessary information

- does not include many details

- is written in your own words

Step

3

Use the following prompt to complete the prewriting and writing activities:

Read the passage "Malik's Machine" on page 115 and write a summary.

Step

4

Complete the graphic organizer on page 116 as your prewriting activity. Use your graphic organizer to help you think through your summary of "Malik's Machine."

         © 2005 Englefield & Associates, Inc.

Step

3

Malik's Machine

When Malik's family saw his "time machine," they all laughed. Anybody would have laughed looking at the mass of cardboard and duct tape sitting in the Johnsons' backyard. There was nothing scientific about an old refrigerator box. "You're wasting your time," said Malik's brother, Jamal.

Alone in the yard, Malik looked at his time machine. There was a tear where his brother had lifted the hatch and tried to get inside. The cardboard was looking a little soggy from the morning dew. Even Malik had to admit it didn't look like much, but his mom always said to him, "What's on the outside does not matter; it's what's on the inside that counts."

Slowly, Malik climbed inside the main compartment and closed the hatch door carefully. After pressing a few buttons and setting a few dials, he pulled the final lever. As if it had come to life, the time machine churned and shook. Malik was glad he thought to install the seat belt. The time machine jumped and spun and finally, in a flash of light, Malik and his machine were gone.

When dinner time rolled around, Mrs. Johnson told Jamal to call Malik. Jamal peered into the backyard expecting to find Malik playing in his time machine, but Malik and the machine were both gone. Good, thought Jamal, that kid finally realized that playing 'time machine' was stupid and cleaned up his mess.

Jamal walked around the yard looking for Malik, when suddenly he was engulfed in a green fog. The ground beneath his feet began to shake. Jamal was scared, but soon everything stopped. Right in front of him was Malik's time machine. Jamal thought he was seeing things. That time machine had not been there two minutes ago. The hatch door popped open and out jumped his younger brother, all smiles. Malik handed him a piece of rope. When Jamal saw what was tied to the other end of the rope, his jaw dropped. He vowed he would never doubt his little brother again—there was a baby Triceratops sitting in the middle of his backyard!

Steps for Writing a Summary

Only the Main Ideas

Topic: _____

Complete the Following Steps:

Step 1 ☐ Skim the reading selection and begin to look for the main idea.

Step 2 ☐ **Underline the topic sentence for each paragraph in the text selection.** (If there is no topic sentence, write one for the paragraph.)

Step 3 ☐ **Cross out unimportant information in the text selection.**

Step 4 ☐ **Cross out information that is repeated.**

Step 5 ☐ **Write what the text selection is about. Include only important information.**

Use the information from your graphic organizer to complete your summary.

Writing Activity 17

Step

5

_____

_____

_____

_____

_____

_____

_____

_____

_____

_____

_____

_____

_____

_____

_____

_____

_____

_____

_____

_____

If you need more room, continue on the next page.

Writing Activity 17

Step

5

Step
6

The checklist shows what your best summary must include. Use the checklist below to review your work.

Checklist for Writing Activity 17

☐ My summary has a sentence that identifies the topic of the text selection.

☐ My summary states the main ideas of the text selection.

☐ My summary does not include information that is not important to the story.

☐ My summary has an ending.

☐ I try to spell words correctly without using any help.

☐ I use interesting words.

☐ My sentences and proper names begin with a capital letter.

☐ My sentences end with a period, an exclamation point, or a question mark.

☐ I have written my summary so the reader can read my print or cursive writing.

Writing Activity 18: Thank-You Note

Step

1

Follow along as the thank-you note below is read aloud.

February 12, 2006

Dear Grandma and Grandpa,

I am writing to thank you for the inline skates you bought me for my birthday. I have been asking for a pair every birthday and holiday that I can remember. Mom and Dad always told me that I would have to wait until I was twelve, so I never dreamed I'd get the skates this year for my eleventh birthday.

When I opened my present from Mom and Dad, I thought a helmet and kneepads were strange gifts. After I tore open your package and saw those shiny, black inline skates lying in the middle of all of the packing peanuts and wrapping paper, their gifts made sense. Dad was afraid they had ruined the surprise for me, but I was so excited to have my own pair of inline skates a year ahead of schedule that nothing could have ruined the day for me.

I pulled on the skates as soon as I kicked off my slippers. I must have looked funny trying to skate around the living room in my pajamas. Mom was not happy with the lines the wheels left in her new white carpet. She said that I could practice in the basement until the snow melts, but she didn't want anymore skating in her living room. Spring will be here soon though, and I can hardly wait to try them outside.

Thank you again for the great gift!

Skating in the living room (sort of!)

Love,

Cyrus

Step
2

There are several things to keep in mind as you plan and write your own thank-you note. Remember, a good thank-you note has the following parts:

- the date

- a greeting or salutation

- a body

- a closing

- a signature

Step
3

Use the following prompt to complete the prewriting and writing activities:

> **A business person has donated money to your classroom for the purchase of computers. Write a thank-you note to this person, the president of a local company, for the generous donation. Explain why you are thankful and how you will use the new technology in your classroom.**

Step
4

Complete the graphic organizer on the next page as your prewriting activity. Use your graphic organizer to help you think through your thank-you note.

Thank-You Note

Date:

Greeting or Salutation:

Body—What you are thankful for and why:

Closing:

Signature:

© 2005 Englefield & Associates, Inc.

Use the information from your graphic organizer to complete your thank-you note.

Writing Activity 18

Step

5

_____

_____

_____

_____

_____

_____

_____

_____

_____

_____

_____

_____

_____

_____

_____

_____

_____

_____

_____

_____

If you need more room, continue on the next page.

Writing Activity 18

Step

5

_____

_____

_____

_____

_____

_____

_____

_____

_____

_____

_____

_____

_____

_____

_____

_____

_____

_____

_____

_____

Step 6
The checklist shows what your best thank-you note must include. Use the checklist below to review your work.

Checklist for Writing Activity 18

☐ I use the form for a letter with the date, a greeting, a body, a closing, and a signature.

☐ My thank-you note tells my reader why I am writing and makes a personal comment.

☐ My thank-you note explains why I am thankful.

☐ My thank-you note includes a personal closing comment.

☐ My thank-you note is well organized and complete.

☐ I try to spell words correctly.

☐ I use words that make my meaning clear. I do not use the same words over and over.

☐ I use correct punctuation and capitalization.

☐ I have written my thank-you note so the reader can read my print or cursive writing.

Writing Activity 19: Thank-You Note

Step

1

Follow along as the thank-you note below is read aloud.

March 6, 2007

Dear Mr. and Mrs. Parker,

Thank you for making me feel so welcome in your home last weekend. The trip to the amusement park on Saturday was so much fun! It was my first time riding roller coasters. The Beyond Gravity ride was as thrilling as everyone said it would be. I can't believe I learned how to surf at the water park's North Shore Adventure! The wave machine was really a wonder to see.

I told my mom how good Mr. Parker's chocolate chip pancakes tasted on Sunday morning. Mom said I've talked about that breakfast so much, she's going to call Mr. Parker for the recipe. Thank you again for making me a part of your family. I had a great time!

Sincerely,

Lu

in front of the Beyond Gravity roller coaster!

Step 2

There are several things to keep in mind as you plan and write your own thank-you note. Remember, a good thank-you note has the following parts:

- the date

- a greeting or salutation

- a body

- a closing

- a signature

Step 3

Use the following prompt to complete the prewriting and writing activities:

> **Thank a friend, teacher, or family member for the support, kindness, or gesture of friendship he or she has shown you. Explain what you are thankful for and why.**

Step 4

Complete the graphic organizer on the next page as your prewriting activity. Use your graphic organizer to help you think through your thank-you note.

Thank-You Note

Date:

Greeting or Salutation:

Body—What you are thankful for and why:

Closing:

Signature:

Use the information from your graphic organizer to complete your thank-you note.

Writing Activity 19

Step

5

If you need more room, continue on the next page.

Writing Activity 19

Step

5

_____

_____

_____

_____

_____

_____

_____

_____

_____

_____

_____

_____

_____

_____

_____

_____

_____

_____

_____

_____

_____

_____

_____

_____

Step
6

The checklist shows what your best thank-you note must include. Use the checklist below to review your work.

Checklist for Writing Activity 19

☐ I use the form for a letter with the date, a greeting, a body, a closing, and a signature.

☐ My thank-you note tells my reader why I am writing and makes a personal comment.

☐ My thank-you note explains why I am thankful.

☐ My thank-you note includes a personal closing comment.

☐ My thank-you note is well organized and complete.

☐ I try to spell words correctly.

☐ I use words that make my meaning clear. I do not use the same words over and over.

☐ I use correct punctuation and capitalization.

☐ I have written my thank-you note so the reader can read my print or cursive writing.

© 2005 Englefield & Associates, Inc.

The Persuasive Communication Process

(Letter to the Editor and Persuasive Paper)

What is the Persuasive Communication Process?

The purpose of the persuasive communication process is to change how the reader thinks or feels about something. Two forms of the persuasive communication process are the letter to the editor and the persuasive paper.

The major difference between these two modes is that a **letter to the editor** is written to the editor of a newspaper or magazine in letter format. **Persuasive papers** include information you want readers to know about. You use the persuasive communication process when you want to persuade to agree with how you think or feel about a particular topic.

You can find examples of persuasive papers in editorial columns of newspapers or magazines, publications and position papers of special interest groups, infomercials, and other forms of advertising. Topics of persuasion often include current political and social issues.

Features of a Letter to the Editor and a Persuasive Paper

- You must state your thoughts and feelings on an issue.

- You must provide reasons that support your thoughts and feelings. The reasons should be based on facts.

- You should understand the "other side's point of view" when you write your persuasive arguments.

- A letter to the editor is written in the format of a letter.

Language of Persuasion		
It is my belief that…	On the other hand	What is your point?
In my opinion…	State	However
As noted…	Opinion	Yet
As you can see…	I see your point	I doubt
In conclusion…	For these reasons	Argue
Pro	Point of view	Con

Writing Activity 20: Letter to the Editor

Step

1

Follow along as the letter to the editor below is read aloud.

May 30, 2006

Dear Editor,

I am writing to bring to your attention the need for a city-wide effort to "clean up" our community. Litter is filling our streets, our parks, and our neighborhoods. Does anyone in City Hall have a plan for tackling this litter problem?

We need to set a positive image for members of our community. We need to let people know we are proud of where we live, and littering in our community is wrong. I want my little brothers and sisters to grow up in a clean and safe community.

I am making three recommendations for City Hall to consider regarding this littering problem:

1. Place more trash cans around the city to discourage people from disposing of their trash on the ground.

2. Pass a city law that fines anyone who litters.

3. Display "Don't Litter" and "Keep Our Neighborhood Clean" awareness signs throughout the city.

I hope that City Hall and the residents of our community will think long and hard about a solution to this growing litter problem.

Sincerely,

Everett Meyers

Step
2

There are several things to keep in mind as you plan and write your own letter to the editor. Remember, a good letter to the editor has the following parts:

- the date, a greeting, a body, a closing, and a signature

- a statement of your opinion

- support for your opinion with facts and statements

- a conclusion that restates your opinion; it may include a suggestion for what needs to be done

Step
3

Use the following prompt to complete the prewriting and writing activities:

> **Write a letter to the editor of your community newspaper. Take a stand for or against the following issue: "There should be more activities for young people in our community."**

Step
4

Complete the graphic organizer on the next page as your prewriting activity. Use your graphic organizer to help you think through your letter to the editor.

Letter to the Editor

Date:

Greeting:

Personal comment (include why you are writing):

Details

First:

Second:

Third:

Personal comments ending the letter (include a restatement of why you are writing):

Closing:

Signature:

Use the information from your graphic organizer to complete your letter to the editor.

Writing Activity 20

Step

5

_____

_____

_____

_____

_____

_____

_____

_____

_____

_____

_____

_____

_____

_____

_____

_____

_____

_____

_____

_____

_____

If you need more room, continue on the next page.

Writing Activity 20

Step

5

Step

6

The checklist shows what your best letter to the editor must include. Use the checklist below to review your work.

Checklist for Writing Activity 20

☐ My letter tells why I am writing this letter to the editor.

☐ My letter tells why I believe my opinion or information is important.

☐ I state my opinion with facts and examples or important reasons.

☐ I restate my opinion in my conclusion and say what I would like to happen.

☐ I use the form for a letter with a date, a greeting, a body, a closing, and a signature.

☐ My letter to the editor is well organized and complete.

☐ I use words that make my meaning clear. I do not use the same words over and over again.

☐ I try to spell words correctly.

☐ I use correct punctuation and capitalization.

☐ I have written my letter so that the reader can read my print or cursive writing.

Writing Activity 21: Letter to the Editor

Step

1

Follow along as the letter to the editor below is read aloud.

September 5, 2007

Dear Editor,

The decision to remove so-called "unhealthy" beverages from our vending machines at the schools in our community is not as black and white as some people think.

First, the chocolate milk and fruit juices in the vending machines have a high calorie count due to the sugar they contain. Students can drink only chocolate milk and juices and still have negative health effects.

Second, milk and fruit juices are not always the best choice for every student. Sometimes, soft drinks may be the best choice when considering different health conditions of students. For example, some students have milk or fruit allergies; students with diabetes need choices related to sugar; and asthmatics need caffeine when they are having an attack. Soft drinks provide choices with caffeine and sugar. Some have caffeine and sugar and others don't, so having choices would be helpful.

Third, the students who make bad choices can still make bad choices at school or when they leave the building. I understand that many students make bad choices and drink only beverages that are full of caffeine or beverages that are high in calories due to sugar; however, not all students make bad choices. I think students should have the right to choose. Since all soft drinks have been removed and the only remaining choices are milk or fruit juice, that right has been taken away.

In summary, I think it is fine that we now have milk and juice as beverage choices, but I think the soft drink choices should be available in our schools as well. Students should have the right to choose. Please consider changing this policy.

Respectfully,

Nadia Rees

Step

2

There are several things to keep in mind as you plan and write your own letter to the editor. Remember, a good letter to the editor has the following parts:

- the date, a greeting, a body, a closing, and a signature

- a statement of your opinion

- support for your opinion with facts and statements

- a conclusion that restates your opinion; it may include a suggestion for what needs to be done

Step

3

Use the following prompt to complete the prewriting and writing activities:

> **Write a letter to the editor of your school newspaper with suggestions about how to welcome new students when they come to your school. Be sure to give specific suggestions about things that could be done by administrators, teachers, and/or students to make the new student and his or her family feel like they belong.**

Step

4

Complete the graphic organizer on the next page as your prewriting activity. Use your graphic organizer to help you think through your letter to the editor.

Letter to the Editor

Date:

Greeting:

Personal comment (include why you are writing):

Details

First:

Second:

Third:

Personal comments ending the letter (include a restatement of why you are writing):

Closing:

Signature:

Use the information from your graphic organizer to complete your letter to the editor.

Writing Activity 21

Step

5

If you need more room, continue on the next page.

Writing Activity 21

Step

5

_____

_____

_____

_____

_____

_____

_____

_____

_____

_____

_____

_____

_____

_____

_____

_____

_____

_____

_____

_____

_____

Step

6

The checklist shows what your best letter to the editor must include. Use the checklist below to review your work.

Checklist for Writing Activity 21

☐ My letter tells why I am writing this letter to the editor.

☐ My letter tells why I believe my opinion or information is important.

☐ I state my opinion with facts and examples or important reasons.

☐ I restate my opinion in my conclusion and say what I would like to happen.

☐ I use the form for a letter with a date, a greeting, a body, a closing, and a signature.

☐ My letter to the editor is well organized and complete.

☐ I use words that make my meaning clear. I do not use the same words over and over again.

☐ I try to spell words correctly.

☐ I use correct punctuation and capitalization.

☐ I have written my letter so that the reader can read my print or cursive writing.

Writing Activity 22: Letter to the Editor

Step

1

Follow along as the letter to the editor below is read aloud.

February 22, 2007

Dear Editor,

I am writing this letter to bring your attention to the need for more sidewalks in our city's neighborhoods. Due to the lack of sidewalks, our residents risk danger each time they walk, jog, or inline skate on our city streets.

In addition, traffic is becoming more and more congested as car and truck drivers come to near halts when attempting to pass a runner or cyclist. I am concerned for the safety of people in this community, especially when pedestrians and motorists are forced to use the same roadways.

Neighborhoods throughout our community consist of families, many with young children. It is important for these children to have safe areas to skate and walk. Many children, who are not permitted on streets, walk through neighbors' lawns.

I know there are several people in my neighborhood whose grass is being trampled because of repeated foot traffic from neighborhood kids. I'm sure these community members would really appreciate more sidewalks on which children could travel.

We must make a change for the safety and convenience of our community members. My grandfather tells me a Development Trust was set up a few years ago to enrich this community. Please consider using money from the trust to build more sidewalks. Thank you for considering my recommendation.

Sincerely,

Shailey Chitluri

Step 2

There are several things to keep in mind as you plan and write your own letter to the editor. Remember, a good letter to the editor has the following parts:

- the date, a greeting, a body, a closing, and a signature

- a statement of your opinion

- support for your opinion with facts and statements

- a conclusion that restates your opinion; it may include a suggestion for what needs to be done

Step 3

Use the following prompt to complete the prewriting and writing activities:

> **Many students feel it is important to wear the latest designer clothing that is often very expensive. Write a letter to the editor of your school newspaper. In your letter, take a position on this statement: "Who you are is more important than what you wear."**

Step 4

Complete the graphic organizer on the next page as your prewriting activity. Use your graphic organizer to help you think through your letter to the editor.

Letter to the Editor

Date:

Greeting:

Personal comment (include why you are writing):

Details

First:

Second:

Third:

Personal comments ending the letter (include a restatement of why you are writing):

Closing:

Signature:

Use the information from your graphic organizer to complete your letter to the editor.

Writing Activity 22

Step

5

_____

_____

_____

_____

_____

_____

_____

_____

_____

_____

_____

_____

_____

_____

_____

_____

_____

_____

_____

If you need more room, continue on the next page.

Writing Activity 22

Step

5

         © 2005 Englefield & Associates, Inc.

Step

6

The checklist shows what your best letter to the editor must include. Use the checklist below to review your work.

Checklist for Writing Activity 22

☐ My letter tells why I am writing this letter to the editor.

☐ My letter tells why I believe my opinion or information is important.

☐ I state my opinion with facts and examples or important reasons.

☐ I restate my opinion in my conclusion and say what I would like to happen.

☐ I use the form for a letter with a date, a greeting, a body, a closing, and a signature.

☐ My letter to the editor is well organized and complete.

☐ I use words that make my meaning clear. I do not use the same words over and over again.

☐ I try to spell words correctly.

☐ I use correct punctuation and capitalization.

☐ I have written my letter so that the reader can read my print or cursive writing.

Writing Activity 23: Persuasive Paper

Step

1

Follow along as the persuasive paper below is read aloud.

Skateboarders' Dilemma

I believe that skateboarders in our community are not being treated fairly. Skateboarding is a wholesome outdoor sport and a great form of exercise. More and more of my peers are becoming worried about the fact that skateboarding is being banned all over our town.

My friends and I have searched everywhere for a place to skateboard and are constantly being told we are not permitted to skate on private or public property. Last summer we skateboarded on the school parking lot. Over the summer, the school building and the parking lot were both empty. We were always respectful, never damaging or hurting anything. But when this summer approached, signs were posted stating skateboarding had been banned on school grounds. We thought we could take our hobby to public parks, but they had signs indicating skateboarding was against the rules. We found similar signs at other parking lots and public places throughout the community.

Skateboarding is a sport just like any other that requires a great deal of skill and practice. We feel skateboarders are being treated unfairly. Bicycling, jogging, and inline skating are allowed in public parks, but skateboarding is not. If you are going to ban skateboarding from public places, please give kids somewhere they can skateboard.

The neighboring community of Sierra built a skateboarding complex for local teens about two years ago. The money to build the complex was raised by teens and their families as well as members of the Parks and Recreation Board, the mayor, and his staff. The skateboarding area in Sierra is a huge success. The skateboarders respect the area and often invite members of the community to watch their practice sessions. The area helps everyone appreciate this unique sport.

I think our community should consider building a skateboarding area. The area would provide a safe place for kids to skateboard and have fun with their peers. If we look at the example set by the community of Sierra, we can see that a skateboarding area is a good idea for our town.

Step

2

There are several things to keep in mind as you plan and write your own persuasive paper. Remember, a good persuasive paper has the following parts:

- a statement of your opinion

- support for your opinion with facts and statements

- a conclusion that restates your opinion (it may include a suggestion for what needs to be done)

Step

3

Use the following prompt to complete the prewriting and writing activities:

Choose an important issue facing your community, state, or country. Write a persuasive paper that will convince the reader to agree with your opinion.

Step

4

Complete the graphic organizer on the next page as your prewriting activity. Use your graphic organizer to help you think through your persuasive paper.

Persuasive Paper

Title: _____

Introductory Paragraph (state your opinon):

Reason #1:

Reason #2:

Reason #3:

Concluding Paragraph:

Use the information from your graphic organizer to complete your persuasive paper.

Writing Activity 23

Step

5

_____

_____

_____

_____

_____

_____

_____

_____

_____

_____

_____

_____

_____

_____

_____

_____

_____

_____

_____

_____

_____

If you need more room, continue on the next page.

Writing Activity 23

Step

5

_____

_____

_____

_____

_____

_____

_____

_____

_____

_____

_____

_____

_____

_____

_____

_____

_____

_____

_____

_____

_____

_____

_____

Step

6

The checklist shows what your best persuasive paper must include. Use the checklist below to review your work.

Checklist for Writing Activity 23

☐ My persuasive paper has a statement of my opinion.

☐ I support my opinion with facts, examples, and important reasons.

☐ I organize my support in paragraphs.

☐ I use signal words (first, next, then, in addition, consequently, etc.) that make my writing easy to follow.

☐ I have a conclusion that restates my opinion and says what needs to be done.

☐ My persuasive paper is well organized and complete.

☐ I use words that make my meaning clear. I do not use the same words over and over again.

☐ I try to spell words correctly.

☐ I use correct punctuation and capitalization.

☐ I have written my paper so that the reader can read my print or cursive writing.

Writing Activity 24: Persuasive Paper

Step
1   Follow along as the persuasive paper below is read aloud.

Keesha Smith for Student Council Representative

My name is Keesha Smith, and I am running for Student Council. I think that I would be a good Student Council representative for the students of our school.

I have new and interesting ideas on how we could make improvements in our school. First, I would like to petition the school board to use some of the money from the spring fundraiser to buy new computers for the library. I believe students need to be able to work with computers as much as possible before they go to high school. Second, I would like to start a school newspaper club. All students would be invited to join the club. The newspaper would be a good way to promote the positive things going on in our school. It would also help to keep everyone informed.

Another reason I feel that I would be a good representative on Student Council is I get along well with most people in school, including teachers and other school employees. This would make it easy for me to talk with people about the changes and ideas that I have. I am outgoing and caring, and I will make sure I listen to everyone's ideas. I think that an important part of being on Student Council is listening to the ideas and concerns of students in our school. I promise to bring all those ideas and suggestions to the Student Council's attention. I will work together with other members of the Student Council to make our school the best that it can be.

I have been going to this school since I was in first grade, so I know pretty well how things work around here. I know that Student Council is an important part of our school, and I believe I would be a good representative for the student body. Please keep the name Keesha Smith in mind when you vote for Student Council representatives next week.

Step 2

There are several things to keep in mind as you plan and write your own persuasive paper. Remember, a good persuasive paper has the following parts:

- a statement of your opinion

- support for your opinion with facts and statements

- a conclusion that restates your opinion (it may include a suggestion for what needs to be done)

Step 3

Use the following prompt to complete the prewriting and writing activities:

> **Choose an important issue facing your school or family. Write a persuasive paper that will convince the reader to agree with your opinion.**

Step 4

Complete the graphic organizer on the next page as your prewriting activity. Use your graphic organizer to help you think through your persuasive paper.

Persuasive Paper

Title: _____

Introductory Paragraph (state your opinon):

Reason #1:

Reason #2:

Reason #3:

Concluding Paragraph:

Use the information from your graphic organizer to complete your persuasive paper.

Writing Activity 24

Step

5

_____

_____

_____

_____

_____

_____

_____

_____

_____

_____

_____

_____

_____

_____

_____

_____

_____

_____

_____

_____

_____

_____

If you need more room, continue on the next page.

Writing Activity 24

Step

5

_____

_____

_____

_____

_____

_____

_____

_____

_____

_____

_____

_____

_____

_____

_____

_____

_____

_____

_____

_____

Step

6

The checklist shows what your best persuasive paper must include. Use the checklist below to review your work.

Checklist for Writing Activity 24

☐ My persuasive paper has a statement of my opinion.

☐ I support my opinion with facts, examples, and important reasons.

☐ I organize my support in paragraphs.

☐ I use signal words (first, next, then, in addition, consequently, etc.) that make my writing easy to follow.

☐ I have a conclusion that restates my opinion and says what needs to be done.

☐ My persuasive paper is well organized and complete.

☐ I use words that make my meaning clear. I do not use the same words over and over again.

☐ I try to spell words correctly.

☐ I use correct punctuation and capitalization.

☐ I have written my paper so that the reader can read my print or cursive writing.

Writing Activity 25: Persuasive Paper

Step **1** Follow along as the persuasive paper below is read aloud.

Pet Ownership Equals Important Responsibility

Five months ago, my neighbors bought a playful German Shepherd puppy from the mall pet store. They named him Max because he was active to the "max." By the time the dog was only five months old, he had chewed twelve pair of shoes, damaged the family room couch, and scratched two doors in the house. After Max had eaten every flower in the yard, my neighbors decided that it was time to find Max a new home. Families should carefully consider the responsibilities of bringing a dog into a family.

One problem that pet owners face is that owning a puppy is much more than making certain the dog has food and water. A dog like Max requires his owners to provide obedience training and attention. Max spent many hours in the house by himself. He damaged items because he did not have adequate training or enough attention from the family. Unfortunately, his owners became frustrated with his behavior.

Another problem that Max's owners faced was finding a good home for him. Since Max was already five months old, he had established behavior patterns that would be difficult to change. Luckily for Max, an experienced dog trainer agreed to take him. The trainer had to spend many hours working with Max to train him to become an enjoyable pet.

Pet owners need to consider both their lifestyle and ability to care for the selected pet. Our neighbors probably needed to consider a smaller dog or another pet that would require less time.

Pets can bring happiness and joy to their owners. Unfortunately, if all factors are not considered, the animal can cause problems. Before family members bring a dog or any other cute baby animal into the family's home, they should consider all the needs of the animal for many years.

Step
2

There are several things to keep in mind as you plan and write your own persuasive paper. Remember, a good persuasive paper has the following parts:

- a statement of your opinion

- support for your opinion with facts and statements

- a conclusion that restates your opinion (it may include a suggestion for what needs to be done)

Step
3

Use the following prompt to complete the prewriting and writing activities:

> **You would like to adopt a pet from your community's animal shelter that is sponsoring an essay contest. Choose any pet that you think you would enjoy owning—a dog, a cat, a bird, a fish, or any other animal that you would like to care for as a pet. Write a persuasive paper to the animal shelter that discusses why you would be a good pet owner.**

Step
4

Complete the graphic organizer on the next page as your prewriting activity. Use your graphic organizer to help you think through your persuasive paper.

Persuasive Paper

Title: _____

Introductory Paragraph (state your opinon):

Reason #1:

Reason #2:

Reason #3:

Concluding Paragraph:

Use the information from your graphic organizer to complete your persuasive paper.

Writing Activity 25

Step

5

If you need more room, continue on the next page.

Writing Activity 25

Step

5

_____

_____

_____

_____

_____

_____

_____

_____

_____

_____

_____

_____

_____

_____

_____

_____

_____

_____

_____

_____

_____

_____

Step **6**   The checklist shows what your best persuasive paper must include. Use the checklist below to review your work.

Checklist for Writing Activity 25

☐ My persuasive paper has a statement of my opinion.

☐ I support my opinion with facts, examples, and important reasons.

☐ I organize my support in paragraphs.

☐ I use signal words (first, next, then, in addition, consequently, etc.) that make my writing easy to follow.

☐ I have a conclusion that restates my opinion and says what needs to be done.

☐ My persuasive paper is well organized and complete.

☐ I use words that make my meaning clear. I do not use the same words over and over again.

☐ I try to spell words correctly.

☐ I use correct punctuation and capitalization.

☐ I have written my paper so that the reader can read my print or cursive writing.

Subject-Specific Skill Development
Workbooks Increase Testing Skills

**Write on Target
for grades 1/2,
3, 4, 5, and 6**

**Includes
Graphic Organizers**

**Read on Target
for grades 1/2,
3, 4, 5, and 6**

**Includes
Reading Maps**

Math on Target for grades 3, 4, and 5

Includes Thinking Maps

For more information, call our toll-free number: 1.877.PASSING (727.7464)
or visit our website: www.showwhatyouknowpublishing.com